THE
LEBENSRAUM
PROGRAM

NEIL JENKINS

The Lebensraum Program

ISBN: 9781836022336
Saddle Stitched

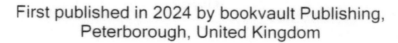

First published in 2024 by bookvault Publishing, Peterborough, United Kingdom

An Environmentally friendly book printed and bound in England by bookvault, powered by printondemand-worldwide

This is a theoretical piece written from a German perspective about the reclamation of their country in 1942, and the implementation of the Lebensraum program.

However, it's not a **'What If'** – it's a **'What Is'**,

All statistics, dates and actions are to the best of my ability accurate. With exception of those I have deliberately changed in order to implement the Lebensraum program within the UK.

Edited by: Rebecca Brown at Pretty and Precise Editing
Republic of Ireland
Maps: Luke William Jones of Dudley, England.

*Inselaffe: *A derogatory term, used in both world wars, for the British.*
*Regierung Von Albion: *Government of Albion.*
*Albionum: *People of Albion*

PART I

My father was in the Diplomatic Corps of the Third Reich from 1936 to 1942. Having spent most of his service in Washington DC, he transferred back to Berlin in 1941, prior to his resignation at the end of the war. His short but distinguished career earned him a place in the Regierung Von Albion upon its independence on May 14th 1942.

I was born at the end of the same year, one of the first free Albionum. It is my father's knowledge and experience which formed the basis of this article, along with my personal friendships and access to information within the government, enabling a brief but accurate account of our country's reclamation.

Shortly after my father had taken up his appointment in Washington, King Edward VIII abdicated. The former King of England's endorsement of Chancellor Adolf Hitler and the Third Reich prompted a wave of popularity that continued for several years.

The peaceful annexation of Austria in March 1938 and the subsequent annexation of Sudetenland (Czechoslovakia) during the following year drew very little attention in the USA. President Roosevelt, more concerned with domestic issues, stated that America would remain neutral and not involve itself in European politics.

There is very little information about Franklin Roosevelt, commonly known as FDR, within any of the known archives of the Third Reich. However, if things had been different (so it was explained) the American president could have been a major obstacle to the Reich and to the foundation of Albion.

Born in 1882, he'd suffered a paralytic illness in the twenties. Over the course of a varied (somewhat colourful) career, he proved an astute and resilient politician and on March 4th 1933 he became America's 32nd President.

However, with a significant wane in his popularity due to his domestic policies, Roosevelt suffered a series of defeats in both the Primaries and 1938 elections. When congress reconvened in March 1939, the Republicans — under Senator Robert Taft (an isolationist) — formed a coalition with Southern Democrats and rendered him virtually impotent.

Due to finish his second term in 1940, he was not viewed as a serious threat to the Reich. That said, even with his hands tied, the actions of the President were to cause alarm on several occasions.

On June 9th 1939, Roosevelt arranged a visit by the British reigning monarch King George VI and Queen Elizabeth (nullifying any further relationship with Edward VIII).

Although in public he was extremely careful in what he said and did, so as not to provoke isolationist sentiment, there was a notable shift in his attitude toward the Third Reich.

On September 1st 1939 the Führer ordered the annexation of Poland. Subsequently both Great Britain and France declared war upon us.

We had been forewarned by the Gestapo of an extremely close relationship between Roosevelt and the British Prime Minister, Winston Churchill. But we were caught by surprise when the President attempted to introduce legislation which would overturn the 1935 Neutrality Act (allowing him to supply arms to the British).

Fortunately (with a little help) a coalition led by an isolationist, Charles Lindbergh, and Senator William Borah managed to defeat the motion.

May 9th 1940, Blitzkrieg. We finally repaid the utter humiliation we had been subjected to in 1918 by annexing Europe. In less than a fortnight, the Inselaffe abandoned their weapons and scuttled across the sea with their tails between their legs.

Unfortunately, our political aspirations in the USA did not fare as well. We had underestimated not only Roosevelt, but more importantly, his wife Eleanor. No president in the United States had ever exceeded two terms in office and Roosevelt had given no indication he would be any different. But in the First Lady's address at the Democratic National Convention in July 1940, Eleanor was to pave the way for her husband to fly in the face of tradition and accept the Democratic party's unanimous support in his bid for re-election. The only saving grace was that lobbyists managed to prevent Henry Wallace (known to be pro-British and Roosevelt's choice) from becoming his running mate and insist that John Nance Gardiner (an isolationist known as Cactus Jack) be put forward for a third term as Vice President.

The first assault by the Luftwaffe was launched upon Britain on July 10th 1940. We had suspicions that Roosevelt, in breach of the Neutralities Act, was sending military aid to the British Isles. This was confirmed less than two months later, on September 2nd, when Roosevelt side-stepped Congress and announced a 'Bases for Destroyers' agreement with Churchill in which America could place military bases in the Caribbean and in return the Royal Navy would receive fifty Destroyers.

When Congress approved the first ever peacetime draft on September 16th, the Führer all but stated that further political involvement in the USA was pointless.
On September 27th 1940 the Tripartite Pact was signed by the Axis powers: Deutschland, the Imperial Japanese, and Italy.

By October 31st 1940 the Luftwaffe conceded that it was no longer able to continue further attacks upon Britain. Adolf Hitler was furious, a growing hatred for the Inselaffe enshrined upon the sinking of his flagship (the *Bismarck*) in the following year.

Not having lost hope, we still placed our full support behind the Republican Candidate Wendell Wilkie in the November 1940 presidential election. His arguments were sound: to allow Roosevelt a third term in office was to set a dangerous precedent; Roosevelt's domestic policies were an absolute shambles; and without doubt, he would take them into another costly European war, wasting millions of American lives.

Unfortunately, Willkie's association with big business alienated the working-class voter and with Franklin Roosevelt's assurance that he would not take them into another war he won a comfortable victory.

My father was not a particularly religious man, but both he and the Third Reich were to thank God on the morning of January 6th 1941. Whilst preparing his State of the Union address, Roosevelt complained of a terrible headache, falling unconscious. He died at 3.35 that afternoon. Two days later his body was transported by train to his birthplace at Hyde Park, and on January 9th 1941 he was buried, per his wish, in the rose garden of his Springwood Estate.

As is required by their constitution, upon Roosevelt's death John Nance Gardiner was sworn in as President. Addressing the United States at 7.30 that evening, he announced a thirty-day period of mourning. Expressing the nation's sorrow and gratitude, he asked God for the strength of mind to complete the work that FDR had started and reiterated their commitment to preventing America being dragged into another war.

On Monday February 10th 1941, President Gardiner reasserted Congress's commitment to the Neutralities Act, inclusive of the 1936 & 1937 amendments, preventing any further shipments of arms to Great Britain.

Cactus Jack — his relationship with the Third Reich enabling a mutually beneficial trading program that would last for decades — was to be re-elected in the 1944 presidential elections.

In July 1941 the Japanese Imperial Army (acting within the Tripartite Pact) commenced its invasion of the Eastern hemisphere. Dutch East India and French Indochina (now under the control of the Third Reich) capitulated, and British Malaya fell within weeks.

OPERATION WALHAZ
MAY 13ᵀᴴ 1942

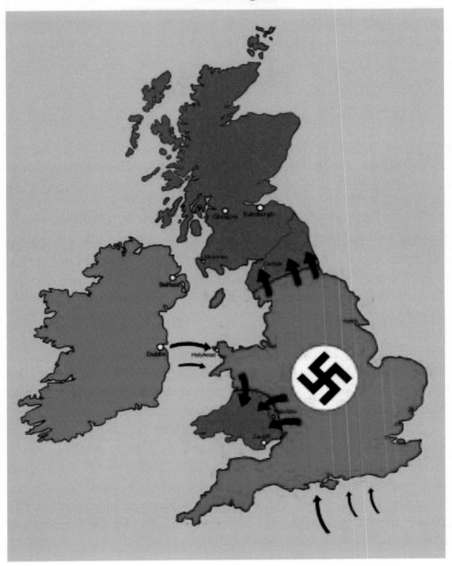

Insula Albionum: Island of Albions (Name prior to Roman Invasion).
Walhaz: Foreigner; non-Germanic speaking.
Wallia: The West of Albion (Roman).
Lebensraum: Living Space (Resettlement)

PART II

Having rekindled the relationship between the Third Reich and the United States, Adolf Hitler turned his attention back to Britain. His priority was the rebuilding of the Luftwaffe and the destruction of the Royal Navy.

On May 24th 1941 the *Bismarck*, pride of the Kriegsmarine, engaged and destroyed the British battleship *HMS Hood,* with the *HMS Prince of Wales* severely damaged and forced to flee. Unfortunately, the Führer's pleasure turned to bitterness three days later when a combination of British battleships and cruisers, backed by the Fleet Air Arm, sank his beloved ship.

In the *Zweites Buch*, published at the end of the war in 1942, the Führer details his thoughts and actions during his renowned table talks, regarding not only the war but its aftermath.
'*Lebensraum*' was not just an idle thought or fantasy. The American expansion into the west was only accomplished because they'd removed the redskins from their land and forced them into reservations. Having pointed in the direction of the coast, he decreed: "Your duty is to Germanise that country, through immigration and the spread of our language, culture, and people. You will treat the *Inselaffe* as the Americans treated their natives."

With the attack by Imperial Japanese in July 1941, the Royal Navy was forced to divide its fleet between Europe and the Eastern hemisphere.

The Luftwaffe, growing stronger by the day, scoured the sea for British ships, increasing its strikes upon the southern coast and the airfields protecting them. The lack of supplies and constant attacks depleted both the British Airforce and Navy's ability to retaliate.

Sunday, March 2nd 1942. The Third Reich launched the largest aerial attack ever witnessed. Thousands of bombers over a period of twenty-four hours were to blacken the skies over London. But it was no ordinary aerial attack: amongst every string of bombs were incendiary devices. The intention was to cause a fire storm, wiping the city and its inhabitants off the face of the earth.

Whatever the depth or strength of the air raid shelters, not a soul would survive. The ferocity of the flames incinerated or asphyxiated every one of them.

On March 4th the Ambassador for the Republic of Ireland was summoned to the Reichstag. A cordial meeting, he was asked one question: *"Verbündeter oder Feind?"* (Enemy or Friend?)

April 1942 was one of the warmest Aprils on record. The clear skies on the 10th signalled the start of 'Operation Walhaz' and the beginning of a relentless aerial bombing campaign. The Luftwaffe were to let loose every aircraft within their arsenal upon the southern and western coasts of England and Wales, from both the Republic of Ireland and France.

On Sunday April 19th the Wehrmacht, accompanied by thirty-eight divisions of the Waffen SS, launched the largest marine-based attack in living history. Backed by the *Tirpitz* (sister ship of the *Bismarck*), the renewed might of the Kriegsmarine, and the Luftwaffe, they'd crossed both the Irish Sea and the Channel, landing on the north coast of Wales and at various points on the southern coast of England.

With the destruction of the British monarchy and the almost complete loss of their government (March 2nd), we expected little resistance. But we warned them, through the mocking broadcasts of William Joyce (Lord Haw Haw), that should we encounter any, we would offer no quarter.

This was not an empty threat. Instructions given by the High Command to the Wehrmacht and the Waffen SS prior to their departure quoted Willhelm II:

"Kommt Ihr vor den Feind, so wird er geschlagen, Pardon wird nicht gegeben; Gefangene nicht gemacht. Wer Euch in die Hände fällt, sei in Eurer Hand."

(If you come before the enemy, he will be defeated! No quarter will be given! Prisoners will not be taken! Whoever falls into your hands is forfeited!)

A brutal and savage campaign, our soldiers were to meet stiff resistance. Our threat failed to create fear but induced hatred: every ditch, every wall became a battlefield. When overrun their women would feign death or hide beneath the rubble and attack us from behind; stories of the *Nachthexen* (night witches) were rife amongst our ranks.

By May 13th 1942, we brought our ground forces to a halt approximately 130 kilometres south of the Scottish border. With every city, town and village north of us as indistinguishable as those in the south (thanks to the heroic efforts of the Luftwaffe), we prepared for the final offensive.

The south of Wales, although bolstered by those who'd escaped across the Bristol Channel and the Severn River, was encircled by a large battlegroup to both the north and east of their enclave. Its inhabitants in no better condition than the *Inselaffe* to the north of us.

On May 14th 1942, they laid down their arms and surrendered. Operation Walhaz and the war were over.

Within months of the war's end and upon the founding of Albion, my father and heavily pregnant mother left Berlin. These were exciting times, Albion being the first Independent State within the Third Reich. My parents would often laugh about the hardships of the first few years, as our country was rebuilt, but they wouldn't have missed it for the world.

The Führer provided unlimited resources and people flocked from across the Reich to a country found to be rich in German heritage. The first Germanic tribes were believed to have colonised 'Insula Albionum' forty-four thousand years ago, with the Druids following their ancestors well before the first Roman invasion in 43AD. But despite the might of the Roman Empire being unable to remove us from the Northern Hills, it wasn't until the Romans left that the Germanic tribes, known as the Angles, once again reclaimed all of their land. A mixture of both Pagan and Druid beliefs, their eventual demise was believed to have occurred with the coming of Christianity.

For our security we retained several divisions of the Waffen SS and a sizable presence from the Luftwaffe. These were to become the core of our armed forces, reinforced by mandatory conscription and a part-time requirement for all adults within the new settlements.

This force proved indispensable in the implementation of the *Lebensraum* program. Lacking the facilities to imprison those who resisted, we transported them back to the Reich, a policy that we were forced to end within two years. After that (much to the annoyance of my father), we were required to house them in prisons or detention camps within Albion. Which meant that those who survived would be placed in the reservations and would ultimately become a serious problem for future generations.

But overall, due to the efficiency and engineering capability of the Reich, the rebuilding and resettlement programs went extremely well. Within two years we'd built the foundations of our capital city, Sarum, and created the city of Angles at the base of the northern hills.

Rebuilt the former Roman cities of Wroxeter (in the west) and Corbridge (in the Midlands).

On Sunday June 20th 1948, Operation Barbarossa commenced, the invasion of Russia by the Axis powers and the United States. Lasting only four months, it had no direct bearing upon Albion. However, following its completion the Führer was to direct his attention, resources, and encouragement to migrating eastward.

Unfortunately, we were not in a position to lose the influx of settlers or the financial assistance of the Reich. It was then that my father and several other members of the Regierung Von Albion were to approach the Americans. I am proud to say that they established a relationship that would be passed through the years to every President of the United States. A friendship that would not only see recurring financial aid to our country in times of trouble, but would open the door to thousands of Americans of German descent (the only downside being our second language became American).

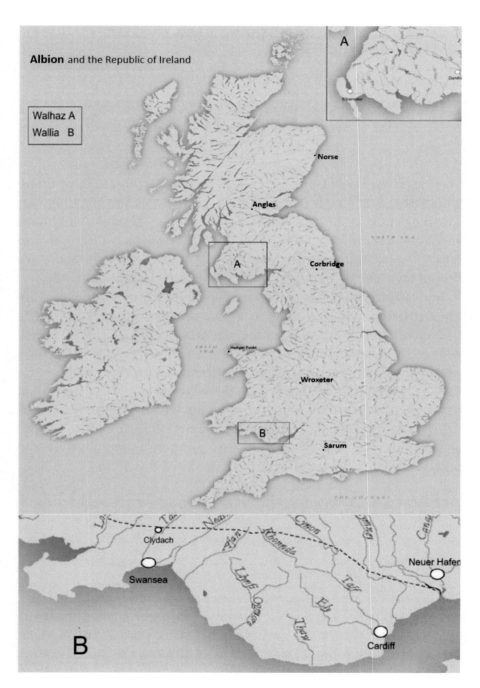

Albion and the Republic of Ireland

Walhaz A
Wallia B

A

Norse

Angles

NORTH SEA

Corbridge

Wroxeter

Sarum

THE CHANNEL

Clydach

Neuer Hafen

Swansea

Cardiff

B

15

*Ryddid: *A known terrorist organisation (Brit word for freedom).*
*Wallia & Walhaz: *Reservations.*

PART THREE

I first met Hermann Göring (Regional Chancellor) in 1967, when he joined the Waffen SS. Having been born in Albion in 1949 but spending most of his adolescence in America, I thought we'd have very little in common. I was wrong. His views displayed a strength and purity I associated with his namesake and my father's generation. We served together for five years and remain close friends to this day.

In 1978, having returned to university in the USA (where he excelled), Hermann was asked to appear on a talk show. The *Inselaffe* had committed a series of atrocities around the world, and they wanted the opinion of the Albionum. At the time the bleeding hearts were complaining about resettlement and our refusal to allow the Red Cross into our detention camps. I watched the show, and could never have been prouder of a countryman, let alone a friend:

"The real core of the conflict is the Brits' unfortunate refusal to accept Albion. If they'd really wanted self-determination, they had both Wallia and Walhaz in which to establish a Brit State."

This interview was to attract the attention of our Diplomatic Corps in the USA and eventually led to his recruitment. He would remain in Washington DC until 1988, not only as the voice of Albion, but friend of several presidents, both present and in the making.

The reservations of Wallia and Walhaz, to which Hermann referred, were festering wounds on a country which had remained peaceful since the end of the war – over eighty years. Of the two, Walhaz was the least troublesome. In the northwest of Albion it stretched from the River Doon to the River Nith (a hundred kilometres wide by 115 deep) and contained approximately 2.5 million; less than half the population of Wallia.

Most of the *Inselaffe* from the north of Albion were transported to the Reich in the two years following the war, or fled by ship to Belfast in the Republic of Ireland. The Irish, inundated with refugees, resorted to holding camps, but eventually requested we relocate them.

On May 14th 1992, to commemorate the end of the war, each country within the Reich was given the opportunity to showcase its success. But with Albion celebrating the fiftieth anniversary of its independence, it was given leave to host a five-day 'Peace Conference'. With heads of state from within the Reich and across the world coming together, we were given the opportunity to display the advances we had made.

The capital, Sarum, was one of the most modern cities in the world, its International Airport the largest in Europe, and yet within its centre (a park which exceeded any other in size) was Stonehenge; a seventh wonder of the world, and tribute to our heritage.

To the west was a land bridge in the form of a tunnel to the Republic of Ireland. Autobahns linked Dublin to the city of Wroxeter and every city within Albion.

The south of our country was rich in agriculture and livestock. The Midlands provided coal and steel, with Corbridge (our second city) highlighting Rome's part in our history with the renovation of the old city and Hadrian's Wall.

On the northeast coast we'd built the new city of Norse, the area having been heavily industrialised since the discovery of gas and oil within the North Sea.

The city of Angles, situated below the northern hills and lakes, formed a base for one of the finest and most successful nature reserves in the world. Thriving on tourism, there would have been very few of the world's leaders who hadn't hunted its large array of animals (reintroduced back into the wild) whilst enjoying a tipple of the finest Albion whisky.

As we entered the millennium the *Inselaffe* continued to cause problems, attacking our citizens both in and out of the country. For the most part they were viewed as terrorists, but their political wing did have a degree of success and we were accused – by countries within the Reich and Americas (not the USA) – of occupying their land in Wallia.

As leader of our country, Hermann Göring's reaction had been swift and to the point:
"Despicable; Germanic people are not occupiers of their own land."

Wallia, at the end of the war, had encompassed an area between the River Severn and the Irish Sea, with the *Inselaffe* still inhabiting at least a hundred kilometres north into the western hills of Albion.

But by early 2000, the *Lebensraum* program had reestablished control of the west coast and with new settlements crossing the Severn River from the east, we'd regained all but an area stretching from the River Loughor to the River Usk. A total of ninety-five kilometres in length, its width varied from as much as seven to thirty kilometres.

We'd always suffered spasmodic ground attacks on our settlements by individuals or small groups, even the odd rocket attack. But due to the severity of the reprisals by the Luftwaffe, they'd become few and far between.

However, in 2007 the *Inselaffe* voted overwhelmingly for Ryddid (a known terrorist organisation) to resume responsibility and govern Wallia. We immediately tightened up border and shipping control, as we suspected that Irish sympathisers were smuggling arms from Cork into Swansea, the second largest of Wallia's cities. But at first, only the rhetoric became more aggressive.

2023. Without doubt, over the years and since coming into power Ryddid had launched several much larger, more sophisticated, rocket attacks. But each had been met by serious reprisals and the

Lebensraum program wasn't affected. However, what was of concern were the attacks on settlers and our soldiers.

We had always encouraged our settlements to expand, and never been critical if they were required to use force or call upon the military.

According to official figures, over the first six months of 2023:

- There had been 520 recorded incidents involving our settlers *(No data as to Brit Fatalities)*.
- The SS had made 1651 military incursions into both Wallia & Walhaz.
- Our forces had regained and demolished 451 permanent structures. (*Recorded Brit fatalities 172*)

There are reports that many of these were children *(nits become lice)*.

October 4th 2023: our troops were instructed to aid in the resettlement of Clydach (eleven kilometres from the coast and seventeen from the river Loughor). Virtually empty, with only eighty-four of its residents remaining, the *Inselaffe* didn't prove troublesome and there were no recorded deaths.

However, following their departure our troops were engaged in a firefight with members of Ryddid (casualties on both sides, but no evidence or reports of fatalities).

On October 7th 2023 Ryddid launched an unprecedented, coordinated attack upon our settlements outside of Wallia. Murdering over one thousand two hundred innocent men, women, and children, they'd targeted a music festival attended by hundreds of young people, many of whom were from countries within the Reich and as far afield as the USA. They were believed to have taken two hundred and forty hostages.

Within our country the initial shock and revulsion grew into a deep anger, its direction not purely the Inselaffe - Hermann was heavily criticised. But in hindsight who could have foreseen such a vicious attack? Fortunately, the world rallied to our side and, sickened by the barbarity of known terrorists, they pledged their support. Of course, the USA went further and offered not only financial assistance but several warships to prevent any further aid reaching Wallia.

Having immediately shutdown both Wallia and Walhaz, we recalled all our reserves. Acquiring the acknowledgement and support from the world that we had every right to defend ourselves and, in doing so, enter Wallia with force in order to destroy Ryddid.

With all forms of entry and exit closed (excluding several ships to allow outside nations to evacuate their people) we cut the power, water and all forms of aid to Wallia. The Luftwaffe began launching air attacks, which are still in operation to this day. Our preparations took several days' and enabled us to give notice prior to the commencement of our ground offensive against Ryddid within the city of Cardiff.

Several months later, and with over thirty thousand of the *Inselaffe* dead, our allies (even the Americans) are losing the taste for war. The stories of the atrocities committed by Ryddid no longer raise the sympathy they once held. And whilst insisting that we are entitled to defend ourselves, our allies (including the USA) are once again suggesting the 'Two State Solution'.

Fortunately, Hermann Göring hasn't given them the time of day:
    "No! The Brits want the annihilation of our country!"

What is most annoying is they know it will never happen – so why give hope to the *Inselaffe*?
    Seriously, are we to tell our people they are to leave the homes and businesses in which they've been for generations? So that those who slaughtered our women and children can have them? That our people should give up the land we have held for thousands of years, a land steeped in our history?

And what part of our country should we give them? The south and Sarum? The northeast and our gas & oil? Or maybe Wroxeter and the land bridge to Ireland?

However, easing the conscience of our allies does have its advantages. Hermann has turned his attention to Swansea and, in recognition of our allies' fears of a humanitarian disaster, has instructed the army to assist in the evacuation of all civilians.

East of the city of Swansea, on the river Neath, Wallia is a mere eight kilometres deep. With the city inhabitable after the war, the land encompassing it and to the west will be ideal for resettlement.

============================

A personal note from the Author.

In Adolf Hitler's second book (which was written but not published) he documented his hopes regarding the *Lebensraum* program. It involved what he considered the reclamation of the East (Poland, Czechoslovakia, Russia).

Within the pages you've just read, I describe how *Lebensraum* was implemented throughout the United Kingdom and how it is possible not just to remove and replace a nation but its very memory.

Whilst in reality Lebensraum has and is being successfully implemented by the Israeli's, within the country once known as Palestine.

The Regional Chancellor, Hermann Göring, is based upon Benjamin Netanyahu. The events within his life, accomplishments and quotes are documented fact.

The adjacent map was recognised and acknowledged as Palestine by the known world prior to and upon, Great Britain fulfilling their mandate on May 14th 1948.

I have added the Gaza Reservation, so you may see the comparison to Wallia. However the West Bank, differs to Walhaz, for it fails to supply the Palestinians even the limited security of a reservation. The annual figures documenting the destruction of their homes, fatalities and incursions by the Israeli military, are available through the United Nations (OCHA). Unfortunately, there is not the same accuracy when relating to the fatalities, life-changing or serious injuries inflicted upon them from the Israeli settlements within their midst.

*"Today more than half a million **'Israeli settlers'** live in the West Bank. Israel maintains full control over 60% of the area, with some roads that only Israeli's can use and checkpoints that restrict the movement of Palestinians."*

Abridged excerpt from an article by the Washington Post

However, the Newspaper describes the Israeli's as **'Jewish Settlers'**. Whilst I cannot refer to a people who embrace and implement Hitler's dream with those of the Jewish faith, any more than I could have referred to the Nazi's as Christians.

I know I will be accused of antisemitism but, whatever its form, I truly believe it is only of use to the Israelis - that without the help of Judaism and the people who live by it, the Palestinians will be ethnically cleansed. For the State of Israel is to Judaism, what Isis is to Islam - Both are a cancer which feed on hate.

I will also point out the Holocaust was very real. Millions of people — men, women and children — murdered in an indescribable and inhumane fashion, and I pray to God we never see its like again.

But would it bring them comfort to know that the man who orchestrated that abomination had his dreams of a new race and *Lebensraum* realised, within the State of Israel and in *their* name?

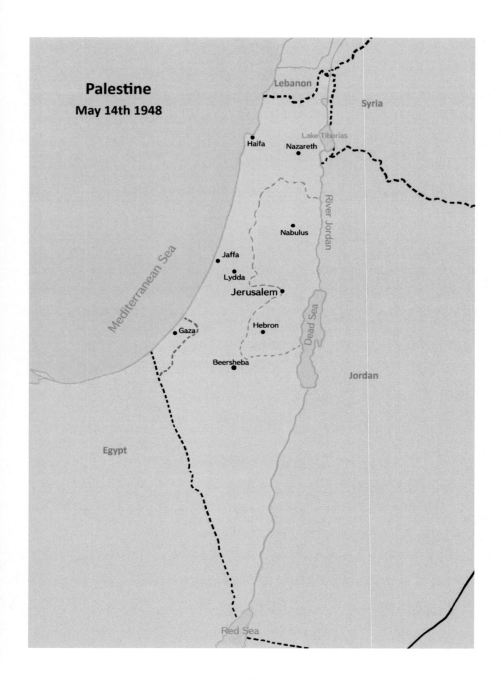